Piano Exam Pieces
ABRSM Grade 4
Selected from the 2023 & 2024 syllabus

Name

Date of ex

Contents

page

Editor for ABRSM: Richard Jones

This book includes audio recordings of all 39 pieces on the Grade 4 syllabus.
To download, please visit shop.abrsm.org/audioredeem and enter the code printed on the inside back cover.

The pieces listed above are just a selection of those on the syllabus that you can choose for your exam; the other options are listed on page 2.

Whether you are taking an ABRSM Practical or Performance Grade, pieces are at the heart of your exam; after all, playing an instrument is all about exploring, performing, and learning through repertoire.

While this book contains nine pieces in a range of styles, the full syllabus has a wealth of other exciting repertoire that we encourage you to explore – to find pieces that really inspire you, that you connect with musically and will enjoy learning, and that will allow you to perform to your very best. You can pick a mixture of pieces from this book and the wider lists if you like – you just need to have one piece from each list, A, B and C.

If you are taking a **Performance Grade**, you also need to prepare a fourth piece which is entirely your own choice. Here you have even more freedom to choose music that really speaks to you, that you want to communicate to others, and that successfully completes your programme. It can be from the syllabus lists, or somewhere else entirely. Just be sure to check the 'Selecting Repertoire' section of the Performance Grades syllabus for important requirements and options for the own-choice piece (like standard and minimum length) and the programme of four pieces overall. Finally, you need to decide what order to play your pieces in and how you, the performer, will take your audience from the very first to the very last note, including moving from one piece to another, so that the performance forms a complete musical journey.

The separate syllabuses are available at **www.abrsm.org**. Whether taking a Practical or Performance Grade, enjoy exploring the possibilities on offer!

First published in 2022 by ABRSM (Publishing) Ltd,
a wholly owned subsidiary of ABRSM, 4 London Wall Place,
London EC2Y 5AU, United Kingdom
© 2022 by The Associated Board of the Royal Schools of Music
Distributed worldwide by Oxford University Press

Music origination by Julia Bovee
Cover by Lloyd Winters, Kate Benjamin & Andy Potts, with thanks to Trinity School, Croydon
Printed in England by Page Bros (Norwich) Ltd, on materials from sustainable sources. P15568

Piano Exam Pieces
2023 & 2024

Other pieces for Grade 4

		Composer	Piece	Publication
A	4	Alcock	Gavot (3rd movt from *Suite No. 2 in Bb*) *with ornaments in bb. 7, 23 & 31; all others optional*	Alcock: Six Suites of Easy lessons (ABRSM) *or* The Best of Grade 4 Piano (Faber)
	5	Beethoven	Allegro assai (1st movt from *Sonatina in F*, Anh. 5 No. 2)	The New Sonatina Book, Vol. 1 (Schott)
	6	Buxtehude	Saraband (from *Suite in E minor*, BuxWV 236)	Baroque Keyboard Anthology, Vol. 1 (Schott)
	7	Dring	Scherzando (from *12 Pieces in the Form of Studies*)	Dring: 12 Pieces in the Form of Studies (Weinberger)
	8	Gurlitt	Allegretto scherzando (3rd movt from *Sonatina in C*, Op. 188 No. 4)	No. 13 from Sonatinas for Piano, Book 1 (PWM)
	9	Haydn	Allegro scherzando in F	Essential Keyboard Repertoire, Vol. 6 (Alfred)
	10	S. Heller	Study in A minor, Op. 45 No. 2	S. Heller: 20 Miscellaneous Studies (ABRSM) *or* pp. 7–9 from Piano Literature for a Dark and Stormy Night, Vol. 1 (Faber Piano Adventures)
	11	G. Berg	Allegro (1st movt from *Sonatina in C*, Op. 3 No. 7)	G. Berg: Twelve Sonatinas, Op. 3, Vol. 2 (Edition HH)
	12	J. F. F. Burgmüller	Ballade, Op. 100 No. 15	Encore, Book 2 (ABRSM) *or* Lang Lang Piano Academy: Mastering the Piano, Level 4 (Faber)
	13	Mozart	Rondo in F, K.15hh	Core Classics, Grades 3–4 (ABRSM) *or* Mozart: 25 Early Pieces (ABRSM) *or* The Best of Grade 4 Piano (Faber)
B	4	C. P. E. Bach	Andante (arr.)	Lang Lang Piano Academy: Mastering the Piano, Level 4 (Faber)
	5	W. Carroll	Sunrise (No. 7 from *River and Rainbow*)	W. Carroll: River and Rainbow (Forsyth)
	6	Granados	Dedicatoria (No. 1 from *Cuentos de las juventud*, Op. 1)	Granados: Stories of the Young, Op. 1 (ABRSM) *or* More Romantic Pieces for Piano, Book 2 (ABRSM)
	7	Khachaturian	A Little Song (Andantino) (No. 1 from *Pictures of Childhood*)	Khachaturian: Pictures of Childhood (Boosey & Hawkes)
	8	Liszt	La cloche sonne, S. 238	Chopin, Liszt, Hiller: Urtext Primo, Vol. 5 (Wiener Urtext)
	9	Mendelssohn	Andante (2nd movt from *Violin Concerto in E minor*, Op. 64), arr. Scott-Burt	Piano Mix 3 (ABRSM)
	10	Vaughan Williams	Valse lente (from *Six Teaching Pieces*)	Vaughan Williams: A Little Piano Book (OUP)
	11	Heather Hammond	Once Upon a Frozen Winter (from *Ballads Without Words*)	Heather Hammond: Ballads Without Words, Vol. 1 (EVC)
	12	Hummel	Romance in G, Op. 52 No. 4	Hummel: 16 Short Pieces (ABRSM)
	13	Trad. Malay	Voyage of the Sampan, arr. Siagian *with repeats*	Malay Folk Songs Collection (Hal Leonard)
C	4	Maikapar	At the Smithy, Op. 8 No. 5	A Romantic Sketchbook for Piano, Book 2 (ABRSM)
	5	Alison Mathews	Buried Rubies (No. 8 from *Treasure Trove*)	Alison Mathews: Treasure Trove (Editions Musica Ferrum)
	6	Martha Mier	Worrisome Blues (from *Jazz, Rags & Blues*, Book 3)	Martha Mier: Jazz, Rags & Blues, Book 3 (Alfred)
	7	Arvo Pärt	Für Anna Maria *fröhlich or nachdenklich*	Arvo Pärt: Für Anna Maria (Universal)
	8	Prokofiev	Marche (No. 10 from *Musiques d'enfants*, Op. 65)	Prokofiev: Musiques d'enfants, Op. 65 (Boosey & Hawkes)
	9	V. Stoyanov	Bulgarian Peasant Dance	The Joy of Modern Piano Music (Yorktown Music Press)
	10	Trad.	Shenandoah, arr. Bennett	The Graded Piano Player, Grades 3–5 (Faber)
	11	Grieg	In the Hall of the Mountain King (from *Peer Gynt, Suite No. 1*, Op. 46), arr. White	Piano Mix 3 (ABRSM)
	12	Kabalevsky	Toccatina (No. 12 from *30 Children's Pieces*, Op. 27)	Kabalevsky: 30 Children's Pieces, Op. 27 (Boosey & Hawkes) *or* The Best of Grade 4 Piano (Faber)
	13	Waller, Razaf & H. Brooks	Ain't Misbehavin', arr. Iles	Nikki Iles and Friends, Book 1 (ABRSM)

Presto

Third movement from Sonata No. 6 in C minor

G. B. Pescetti
(c.1704–66)

Giovanni Battista Pescetti was an Italian composer and keyboard player who studied with Antonio Lotti at St Mark's, Venice, and composed operas for the Venetian theatres. In the 1730s and 40s he worked in London as a harpsichordist and opera composer. He then returned to Venice, taking up an organist's post at St Mark's.

This Presto shows Pescetti's fluent style of writing – and no doubt playing – for the harpsichord or piano (the Venetian source mentions both instruments). All dynamics are editorial suggestions only, as are the slurs in bars 60 and 67, and the slurs to grace notes. The dotted-quaver figures in bar 52 should be played in triplet rhythm to fit in with the rest of the piece; that is, ♩ = ♪.

Sources: MS, *VI Sonate per Clavicembalo o Piano Forte*, Conservatorio di Musica Benedetto Marcello, Venezia, Torr.Ms.B.16; MS, *Sonata VI per il Cembalo*, Sächsische Landesbibliothek, Dresden, Mus. 2967-T-1

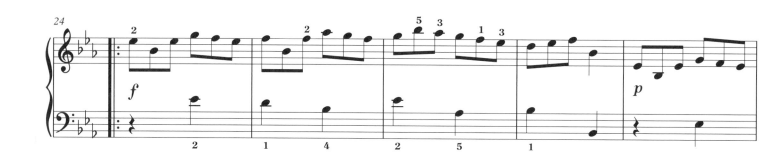

In the Time of a Waltz

Mouvement de valse

No. 15 from *25 études faciles*, Op. 50

Louise Farrenc
(1804–75)

Louise Farrenc was a French pianist who composed many piano and chamber-music pieces. For over 30 years she was professor of piano at the Paris Conservatoire. She says of this piece: 'one should play it in a light and graceful manner'. It is composed in da capo form (ABA), with a *forte* middle section (from bar 17), but the da capo (from bar 39) is written out in full in one of the sources (Leduc). The dynamics in bars 1 and 39 are editorial suggestions only.

Sources: *Études faciles pour piano*, Op. 50, Musique manuscrite Ms. autogr. MS-14286, Bibliothèque nationale de France; *25 études progressives pour le piano*, Op. 50 (Paris: Leduc, 1876)

Allegro in F

HWV 488

G. F. Handel
(1685–1759)

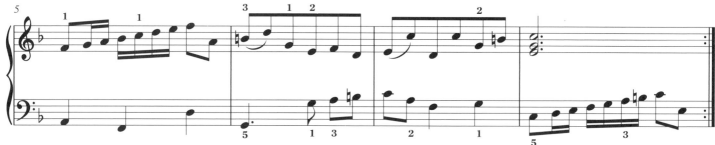

George Frideric Handel composed this dance-like Allegro in London in about 1717. It is written in the style of a 'corrente', a quick dance in triple time and the Italian variant of the French 'courante'. Handel's semiquaver scale figures recall the literal meaning of 'corrente' – 'running'. All slurs and dynamics are editorial suggestions only.

Source: autograph MS, London, British Library, R.M. 20.g.14

Billie's Song

No. 7 from *Portraits in Jazz*

Valerie Capers
(born 1935)

Andante cantabile con moto [♩ = c.58]

mf

with pedal

Bridge

cresc.

Valerie Capers is an American composer, pianist, singer and educator, who studied at the Juilliard School of Music. She is equally at home with jazz and classical music, and has formed her own jazz trio. This is one of the 12 pieces in her collection *Portraits in Jazz*. They 'portray' jazz styles linked to some of the most famous jazz musicians, such as Duke Ellington and Ella Fitzgerald. The 'Billie' in the title of this piece is Billie Holiday.
In the exam, the repeat should be played.

B:2

Idylle

No. 1 from *Album des enfants*, deuxième série, Op. 126

Cécile Chaminade
(1857-1944)

Cécile Chaminade was a French pianist and composer who made her debut as a soloist at the age of 18. She toured France, England and the United States, and, at that time in history, a woman performing her own music was unusual. She composed about 200 piano pieces, which became popular partly because they were easy enough for young pianists at an intermediate level.

This melodious piece, from her *Album des enfants* (Album for the Young), seems to describe a picturesque pastoral scene – a common meaning of the word 'idyll'. It is in ternary form (ABA), with a middle section (bars 16–32) that contrasts in both key and dynamics.

Source: *Album des enfants*, 2me série, Op. 126 (Paris: Enoch, 1907). There is no pedalling marked in bar 18 of the source, but cf. bar 26. The left-hand slurs in bars 17 and 25 are editorial.

© 2022 by The Associated Board of the Royal Schools of Music

The New Doll

La nouvelle poupée

No. 6 from *Album pour enfants*, Op. 39

Edited by Howard Ferguson

P. I. Tchaikovsky
(1840–93)

The Russian composer Pyotr Il'yich Tchaikovsky was clearly following in Schumann's footsteps when he wrote his *Album pour enfants* (Album for the Young) in 1878. The set was subtitled '24 Easy Pieces (à la Schumann)', which means that, while he was composing them, Tchaikovsky must have been thinking of Schumann's *Kinderscenen* (Scenes from Childhood) and *Album für die Jugend* (Album for the Young).

This piece is in ternary form (ABA'): an opening A section in B flat major (bars 1–17); a middle section B, modulating rapidly to other keys (bars 18–33); and a varied reprise of A plus coda (bars 34–57).

Source: *Oeuvres complètes pour le piano*, Vol. IV: *nouvelle edition revue et corrigé par l'auteur* (Moscow: Jürgenson, 1893)

Pentatonic Tune

No. 29 from *For Children*, Vol. 1

Béla Bartók
(1881–1945)

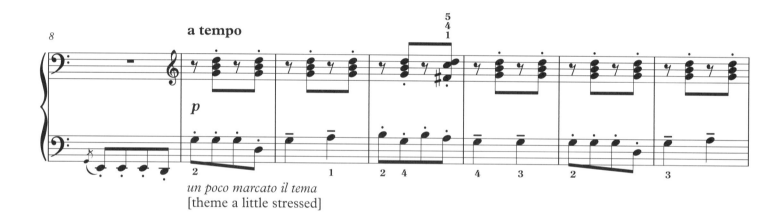

un poco marcato il tema
[theme a little stressed]

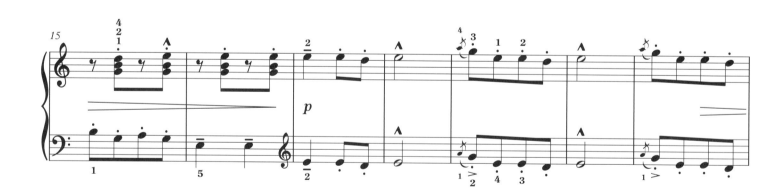

The Hungarian composer Béla Bartók wrote *For Children* between 1908 and 1910. It was his first large collection of folksong arrangements, and contains both Hungarian and Slovak tunes. The composer's aim was to reveal 'the simple and non-Romantic beauties of folk music' to young pianists. He revised the collection in 1943.

'Pentatonic Tune' is taken from Volume 1 of the revised version, which is based on Hungarian folk tunes. The term 'pentatonic' refers to the five-note scale often found in folk music; here it takes the form E-G-A-B-D. Although the composer's metronome mark is ♩ = 138, students may prefer a slower tempo, for example ♩ = c.120.

C:2

Ninette's Musette

No. 5 from *Romantic Impressions*

George Nevada
(1939–2014)

George Nevada, who was of German origin, composed various collections of pieces for solo piano, including *Romantic Impressions*, from which this piece has been selected.

The 'musette' is a type of French bagpipe, popular in pastorales in the 17th and 18th centuries. It also came to mean a pastoral dance piece included in French ballets in the early 18th century. Nevada's style, however, is much more Romantic than that of the original composers of the musette. Although the composer's metronome mark is ♩. = *c*.60, students may prefer a slower tempo, for example ♩. = *c*.44.

Ticklin' Toes

Florence B. Price
(1887–1953)

Florence Price was an African-American composer, pianist and music teacher. She gave her first solo piano recital at the age of 4, and her first composition was published at the age of 11. She studied at the New England Conservatory in Boston and later became head of the music department at Clark University, Atlanta.

First published in 1933, 'Ticklin' Toes' is a lively piece which is derived from African-American dances. It is in ternary form (ABA') and features quirky accents and an often syncopated right-hand part. Although the composer's metronome mark is ♩ = 138, students may prefer a slower tempo, for example ♩ = c.92.